The
Three–Cornered
Shoe

*A Women's Literary Journal Inspired by
The Stories of Rebbe Nachman of Breslov*

BreslovWoman.org

Contents

Letter to The Reader

Dear Reader,

The creative writing in this collection has been inspired by the 13 stories of *Sippurey Maasiot* by Rebbe Nachman, along with some of his shorter tales. Rebbe Nachman's stories are literary, psychospiritual and mystical masterpieces unlike any others, and in these pages, you'll get a glimpse of their ability to touch each reader's inner world. Just as each of us may – and must, if we want to truly grow in closeness to Hashem – find ourselves in the texts of our prophets and sages, we may also find ourselves in Rebbe Nachman's stories and other teachings. Rebbe Nachman himself instructs us to find ourself in Psalms (LM II, 125), and this advice holds true for all authentic Jewish teachings, including and especially, his own works.

But the stories also offer wisdom that transcends self, time and space, and we can understand them as universal teachings that are deeply spiritual and intellectual as well. In his first introduction to *Sippurey Maasiot* published in 1815, Reb Noson writes: "The Rebbe disguised [lofty] and mighty concepts, and hid them in his stories in wondrous, awesome ways. This was the way things were originally done in Israel, through redemption and interchanging. When people wanted to speak of God's hidden mysteries, they would speak in allegory and parable, hiding in many disguises that concealed secrets of the Torah, the King's hidden treasury... [The Rebbe] also said that these stories are chidushim that are very wonderous and awesome. They contain extraordinary, hidden, deep meanings." (Adapted from *Rabbi Nachman's Stories*, The Breslov Research Institute)

From the second introduction, printed in the 1850 edition, which was written before his death in 1844, Reb Noson, referring to the tale, *The Lost Princess*, invites the reader to: "... derive one's own interpretations if one wants, and thus find great encouragement. 'The wise man will hear and expand the lesson' (Proverbs 1:5). The same is true of all the other stories" (Adapted from *Rabbi Nachman's Stories*, The Breslov Research Institute).

This idea, to "derive one's own interpretations if one wants, and thus find great encouragement," is the basis of the workshops that lead to this journal as well as the inspiration for how I teach and personally experience the stories. Although the tales vary in complexity, in general they are meant to be understood at the level of the reader, or rather, the reader's neshama. In fact, Rebbe Nachman told the stories aloud, in Yiddish, the vernacular of his day, so that even the unlearned would be able to understand them at least on the simple level, and find him or herself in them. They are traditionally published in a Hebrew-Yiddish edition.

Time and again I have, as Rebbe Nachman and Reb Noson instruct, sought and found myself in the Rebbe's stories, and it's not an exaggeration to say they've captivated me. The stories have also challenged me intellectually, they've had a profound effect on my emotional and spiritual identity, and they've also simply delighted me. More than a decade ago, I decided to share the stories and other Breslov teachings in an interactive way, modeling the multi-modal approach of the Rebbe, who encourages us to not just learn his teachings but to pray about them and live them fully, with body, mind and soul. After several years of teaching Breslov, I began to create writing prompts based on the stories, and other Breslov texts, and to share them in writing workshops, which have been given at many venues and events. When the Covid lockdowns began, the live programs transitioned to Zoom, which made it easier to offer the workshops to women around the globe. (When Zoom is spelled in Hebrew, it has gematria of 53, the same as gan (garden). And this technology has certainly provided fertile ground, a veritable garden for the writers in the workshops.)

Many of the same women returned workshop after workshop, building trusting relationships with the other participants and finding new and eloquent ways to explore and articulate their innermost thoughts and feelings, especially about their relationship with Hashem. The stories act as a catalyst for the participants' deep exploration of their own perceptions and life-stories, and this leads to fresh – and even life-changing personal discoveries.

For over a decade, BreslovWoman.org has used the following tagline about learning and living with Rebbe Nachman's teachings: *They enable us to heal our relationships with Hashem, with each other, and with ourselves.* For workshop participants, writing from the prompts has become a uniquely effective modality for doing so. No less important, and to my very great joy, the workshops have become a space for the development of lasting friendships. As Rebbe Nachman teaches: *It's very good to talk to a friend*, and especially when one talks to a friend about Hashem and the Rebbe's teachings.

The theme of friendship can be found in these pages. The contributors have also written about the themes of youth and age, family of origin, marriage and children, suffering and redemption, sadness and joy, character development and prayer, humility and simplicity, materialism and spirituality, the Land of Israel, numerous concepts from Torah and much more. There is poetry and prose, there are personal essays (including memoirs, soliloquys and more) as well as creative fantasies and retelling of the stories. There is a wide range of thought-provoking themes born of inspiration as well as a variety of writing styles. I encourage you to read them all – there is something for everyone.

Some of the writers have never written before, others are published authors. The BreslovWoman workshops have in fact helped women become better writers, leading to publication in other venues, but the main goal is quite different – it's about finding, unlocking and actualizing the psychospiritual treasures these stories can confer on both the writer and the reader. The contributors to this collection have so generously given of themselves to you, the reader, and I hope the riches in these pages give you joy and inspire you to read Rebbe Nachman's wonderful stories.

Chaya Rivka Zwolinski, Editor

Summaries of Rebbe Nachman's Stories

The following are very brief summaries containing some important themes from the stories in *Sippurey Maasiot* and other tales, referenced in this journal. Not all 13 stories in *Sippurey Maasiot* are represented here. I encourage you to read the original stories in full and to use these summaries merely as reminders of what the stories are about.

The Lost Princess

The King banishes his daughter from His Kingdom. His trusted viceroy sets out to find her. What is the true object of his search? The Lost Princess has been described as the Shechina, the Jewish nation, the neshama and more. In this most well-known of Rebbe Nachman's stories, we find deep psychospiritual exploration, creation and the secrets of the Torah and Mashiach.

The King and The Emperor

In this story, the emperor's daughter travels the seas. Eventually she returns and is reunited with her husband, the King's son. It's a tale which alludes to the four exiles, the Geulah, the Kabbalistic sefirot and much more.

The Prince of Gems

The characters in this story include a prince made out of gemstones hidden beneath his skin, his father the King, his jealous sister, and a Tzaddik. Spiritual gems are hidden within the story itself: a mystical name of Hashem; Moshe Rabbeinu, and yetziat Mitzrayim; a contemporaneous opponent of Rebbe Nachman's; and much more.

The Sophisticate and The Simpleton

This much-loved story can be understood on the simplest level from beginning to end, although there are many deep mysteries hinting to the ancient but ongoing battle between the Jewish people and our spiritual enemies. The moral of the story? Simplicity leads to happiness in both the material and spiritual worlds, as well as leads to closeness to Hashem. The elemental symbols in this story (such as the cobbler-simpleton's three-cornered shoe hinting to our imperfect service of Hashem – prayer, especially), are beautifully described and bubble up from our memories long after the story is read.

The Exchanged Children

The original prince and pauper classic, this is the story of a prince and a servant switched at birth, their journey through a mystical forest and arrival at a miraculous garden. It tells the deeply psychospiritual tale of how the soul comes down into this world and finds its noble, spiritual self at odds with the coarseness of the body it must call home. Though people connect with some stories more than others, most seem to find a personal connection to, and receive inspiration from, this tale.

The Seven Beggars

Rebbe Nachman said, "If I only told the world this one story, I would still be truly great." *Likutey Halachot, Tefillin 5:1*

This is the story of seven beggars who celebrate the wedding of two orphans they have previously blessed, by blessing them a second time, and telling them astonishing mystical stories within a story. Impossible to describe in a summary, it is a masterful tapestry of many characters and events. This story is complex and transcends time and space.

Summaries of Other Tales

Some of the shorter tales are deceptively simple and others, intricate puzzles. Rebbe Nachman's range of beloved shorter stories are rich with symbols, hints and many layers of meaning. We use prompts based on some of these stories in the introductory, as well as the more advanced, workshops.

The Treasure

A man has a dream about a treasure under a bridge in a faraway town. He travels there and starts digging, but a policeman stops him. He tells the policeman his dream, but the policeman also has a dream of a treasure, and describes it to the man, and the man finds out it's buried in his own backyard!

The Fixer/A Story of Bitachon (Trust)

No matter how much the king thwarts a handyman, he always stays joyful and content, just earning enough for his dinner each night. He also retains his clever sense of humor, and "outsmarts" the king at the end, bringing delight to the monarch.

Simplicity

A king's ministers abandon him in a torrential rainstorm, but a simple woodcutter takes him in. Because of his kindness and willingness to simply serve his guest with the little he has, the woodcutter is the one who receives the honor of escorting the king home and sitting next to his throne.

The Bird

The king, who is a great astrologer, gives the workers plenty of time and everything they need in order to harvest the wheat on time. Instead, the harvesters relax and party, and the wheat harvest doesn't meet the deadline. The workers are worried about the king's reaction but a sage suggests they capture a special bird, the king likes, to appease him. They waste time arguing about how to catch the bird and fail again.

The Diamond/The Clay Digger

A poor man makes his living digging clay. While digging one day, he finds a precious gem. He sails to London in order to sell it. The diamond is mistakenly tossed overboard but the clay digger, who is afraid of the evil ship's captain, puts on a happy face. Before they arrive, the captain trades a load of wheat for the clay digger's diamond (not knowing it has been lost), and then dies. The clay digger is saved, but only because he remains joyful.

Notes

The stories from which the writers drew their inspiration are named at the beginning of each piece. The stories themselves are not published due to space issues. See the acknowledgments to find the sources for the original stories.

The prompts given in the workshops can be guidelines and/or suggestions, and are designed to inspire. They are not published here.

Each of the writers on these pages has a defined style and expression unique to her. English-language spelling differences, such as colour and color, remain. In the phonetic spelling of Hebrew terms, both Sefardic/Modern Hebrew and Ashkenazic Hebrew pronunciations, are the personal choices of the writer with minor revisions for clarity and accuracy. Yiddish spellings too have been revised for clarity and accuracy. Some writers choose a pronunciation to convey a particular emotive experience.

We've included a glossary of most of these Hebrew and Yiddish terms, which also contains brief biographies of some of the personages written about in these pages.

We've included a section called *Your Turn* which contains *Breslov* teachings on the theme of simplicity and introductory warm-up prompts from the BreslovWoman collection, so you can try your hand at writing. Who knows? Perhaps you'll join a workshop, publish your piece or simply enjoy the experience. (I'd be delighted if you shared your writing with me. You can email me at crzbreslov@gmail.com with comments or questions as well.)

Rachel Cohen

Listen my precious daughter, to the instruction of our holy avot, do not forsake the teachings of our loving imahot, and do not abandon the sweet shelter of your Sefer Tehillim.

Let its simple sweetness always be your home in this world, which is masked in complexity and confusion.

Accustom yourself to whispering simple, authentic words to Hashem, from your heart. I pray that this will always bring you back home, no matter how far away you might feel, surrounded in this complicated world of intellectual elites and shiny cities of luxury with no end.

When you have freed yourself from the pressure of the intellect, then the trait of emuna peshuta will begin to enter your heart, and you can begin to distance yourself from the temptation to overthink everything, judge yourself harshly and judge others harshly. Then, it will be easier to love yourself, just how Hashem created you. From there, you can love others and begin to truly love Hashem. Because, as you learned when you were so small, it's all really very simple: V'ahavta l'reiacha kamocha. "Love your neighbor as yourself." *Vayikra 19:18.* That is the entire Torah. But, know, my precious daughter, to fulfill this mitzvah, you must first learn to accept and love yourself. Because if you cannot love yourself first, then how can you love others as yourself?

To love yourself, hug your Sefer Tehillim close and cling to the shelter of simplicity. Close your eyes and your ears to the voices that surround you, pressuring you to achieve intellectual and external perfection. Put a boundary to the allure of prestige and sophistication.

Know, my child, that your worth is not defined by how many mefarshim you can memorize on each pasuk for your Chumash test, how fast you can recite multiplication tables or how well you can put an idea to paper with many fancy words. Know that your essence is not a product of how elegant and made up you might look one day at a simcha, even if it feels nice for a little while (and that's okay). I pray that you find true joy in your learning, satisfaction in your efforts and reasonable hishtadlut, confidence in your abilities, and that you can feel beautiful without shame in the guf that Hashem gave you for your shining neshama—but that you know, none of your achievements (or failures) defines your essence. Please know, my baby, that Hashem just wants your heart and He sees all of you, in your beautiful, simple wholeness since the day you were born.

On the days when it feels like the pressure to "succeed" is overwhelming, and you might feel like you're being pulled far away in different directions—you can open this gift and whisper:

"Hashem is near to those who call with sincerity." *Psalms 145:18.* In these days of confusion and pressure, you can find closeness with these simple words. You don't have to prove anything to be loved.

When you contemplate these things, you will come to love the God who created you and protect yourself from straying far from home, and you can be happy with whatever comes your way. Your emuna peshuta will guard you from pride and the Shechina will rest on you, and others will see it in your face.

Please know, in the words of a king who had the temptations and wisdom of the entire world at his fingertips:

"Beware, making many books has no end, and studying much is a weariness of the flesh … "The end of the matter, everything having been heard, just fear Hashem and keep His mitzvot, for this is the entire man." *Kohelet 12:12-13*

Know that I love you unconditionally with all your simple imperfections, and know that Hashem loves you more.

Signed,

Your mother, a hopelessly complicated woman, striving to break free from the complexity and be a simple Jew

This letter is inspired by Iggeret HaRamban, the letter of Nachmanides to his son.

The Story: The Lost Princess
FINDING RATZON

Find a quiet place
She began
And get very still
She whispered
Write your deepest yearning
She instructed

So I found a quiet place
Tried to begin
I longed to be still
And whispered to myself
What is your deepest yearning?
Just as she asked

First, I was blank
My own ratzon?
My own yearnings?
Desires of my own,
I've not yet formulated them
Could that be the problem?

Second, I protested
I came to you for guidance
At a fork in the road
Needing a wise woman's advice
What does Hashem want from me?
Why should it matter what I want?

Then, I trusted
That your question must be good
I wanted to be still
Just like you asked
But it is so noisy, outside and inside
I am not a good student

Finally, I understood
The noise is the block
It has been so noisy for so long
My deepest desire
My deepest yearning
Is for a little quiet space

A little quiet space
In this world
My deepest yearning
For shalom
For safety
To be me

Good, she said
How did that feel?
To say it out loud?
That desire, you can have
Just remember, she said
He can do anything

About the Author

Rachel Cohen lives in New York with her husband and daughter. She is an artist with a passion for creative writing, who also works as an attorney (where the writing assignments are not quite as exciting as exploring Rebbe Nachman's tales).

Sanam Movtady

Our soul is the daughter of the Emperor, who falls to imprisonment in the palaces of anger, haughtiness, sadness, judgment, complaint, and impatience, among others.

If these emotions and feelings were actually a character in a story, my biggest challenge would be impatience. Not that I have mastered the others, but impatience is the king that relentlessly draws my ship to his palace as I try to pull away.

Noblewomen are assisting the princess to get away, but they don't even know it themselves.

Each one of us is a noblewoman, - assisting others as they seek to find freedom. We are all the princess and the noblewomen at the same time.

The wine is the Torah and the voice of Tzaddikim telling us not to give up the fight. Hopefully all of these battles make us stronger, even if they leave us scarred.

They say life is a journey, not a destination.

The journey is what turns the young, naive princess into a strong, mature queen. A queen who can tame the wild beasts of character flaws into docile servants, there to serve her and her noblewomen, as they endeavor to fulfill their spiritual potential.

A bird, a dove, notified Noach that it's time to get off the Ark and onto the land,

and in time

a bird, an eagle, will deliver us to the Holy Land.

The rest is commentary.

About the Author (Sanam Movtady)

My name is Chana Sara, born in Iran and moved to America about the age of 17, married at 23, and had four children. I'm single again after 35 years. Still trying to figure out life.

Sarah Swartz

The Story: The Diamond/Claydigger
NESTED

I was born in a woodworker's shop just outside Kiev. My father delicately chipped away at the surface of the Linden wood, opening up a cavernous chamber within each of my parts – space to be filled with the depths of myself. He polished each of my layers and glazed them with a kaleidoscope of colours, except for the innermost part, which just had a simple white varnish. Making a matryoshka doll takes a long time, and I took longer than most. Abba finally put me on the shelf of his shop next to the rest of the dolls. I watched silently for years, as everything else in the store – the salt and pepper shakers, the jewelry boxes, and even the paperweights – flew off the shelves. By the time I left the shop, the openings within me hadn't been revealed in years. I was starting to wonder if they still existed. Finally, I was purchased by a family of land-owners with a large estate. I would reside in the bedroom of the smallest girl.

Her bedroom was filled with other dolls, but they weren't like me. They were made from ceramic, with braids down the back, and long eyelashes, and real arms and legs. I was the only doll made of wood, and the smallest by far. One day while playing, the little girl dropped me. She wasn't playing with me at the time – I was collecting dust on the mantle – but she bumped into me, shattering me into pieces on the floor. It wasn't painful at all. In fact, it was pleasant. I felt the colourful walls surrounding myself shatter, one by one, with a sense of calm, tranquility. "That wasn't me to begin with," I thought. The only piece that remained without a crack was the tiny white cylinder at my centre, the one I forgot was ever there. The one my father painted all those years before.

About the author

Sarah Swartz is a student in Toronto, Canada. Her writing is inspired by Pnimiyus haTorah, particularly the teachings of Rebbe Nachman.

Evelyn Luchs

The little sin that holds much,
I found it this year on Yom Kippur.
It is to scoff; act scornfully.
All these years I beat my chest
for the important ones:
the sin of wrongful eating,
baseless hatred, evil inclinations
For years I worked on respect for parents and teachers.
No one likes to be criticized.
I am a parent and teacher and know
it is - our job.

And yet I feel contempt.
Scorn and contempt for whom?
How dare they think that I might fail,
trail behind, be a flop.
It was me who turned their well-meant warnings,

into self-reproach.
Long after my parents said
they were proud of me, knew I would succeed,
I still remember everything.

And now the harshest critic of me is me.
It's a little sin to scuff my way through the morning
and further into the day;
To not get up and pray, but to complain.
But this is the little sin that holds many bigger ones:
The sin of procrastinating: I don't think I can,
at least not today. Maybe tomorrow.
Why even try?
And with that I can make another
do everything himself or for both of us.
And with that can come hardness of heart,
To not admit when one is wrong,
To not care that I may be enslaving another.

"I'm sorry" is by now an insincere confession
if I don't think I can but still promise to do better.
And this leads to coveting my neighbor's almost everything
because they're not like me.
Their house is neater, more up-to-date
so I cast a begrudging eye.
And my counsel can be unintentionally evil
if I don't pay enough attention to give advice
but do so anyway.

A light head alternates with a heavy heart,
and that gives way to confusion of the heart.
And baseless hatred has found its base in me.
To scoff at oneself can lead to not extending a hand
because I want someone to extend their hand to me.
This sin that is scoffing leads to almost all sins
and to the biggest one of all; not being happy.

If the worst critic of myself is me,
And "Happy are those who are at peace with themselves,"
Then someday I will be happy.

The Story: The Lost Princess
AS IT SHOULD BE

After a good night's sleep
I see the world as it should be;
All In order, with God above
and a few noble souls
Who cannot be bribed
by money or pride
Who fight immorality
and ignore profanity
to steer us through this flood.

The Story: The Treasure
AS WOMAN AS CHILD

Sun, Grass, Moon,
Spoon of smooth or lumpy
New or familiar
becomes an elixir.
Womb turned inside out
Nourishes from outside
Light, Love, Music,
Songs and nursery tales,
Rhymes and Rhythms
turn scary into hilarity,
Bring the world on gradually

With Grandma to watch,
Little One won't climb high
or wander far
or eat a bug.
Happy travels for the young one
watched over by an old one
who once traveled the world

The Story: The Prince of Gems
FAIRY TALES

In secret I read Hasidic tales;
Princesses, gems, a frog
Wise men and foolish kings
All to make us think about God

In my mind is also the old,
What I was told
on my first day of school,
Don't tell anyone you're Jewish.

My father saw me fast on Tisha B'av,
arched his eyebrows at the Above,
and said, *You'll go to heaven,*
but you won't find me there.

The kindest most humble man
I have ever known
Didn't care about religion
but allowed it in his home.
To set things straight he said
Even the Bible is man-made.

He told me not to hate;
The good Lord makes all kinds of people
He said of those he could tolerate
Surely, he knew what people were made of—
Cells—so intricate and marvelous,
Who else could have made us but God

About the Author

Evelyn Luchs was born and raised in Salt Lake City by her German-Jewish parents. As part of a small and proud Jewish community, she knew she wanted to live a fully Jewish life. Once she moved to Boston, it became possible. She lives in Boston with her husband, and her son and family live nearby, so she can be a hands-on "Omi", which gives her a lot to write about and think about. She was a philosophy major at the University of Colorado and has her master's degree in psychiatric nursing. She's worked with individuals and families as a psychiatric nurse clinical specialist for the past twenty-five years. Her favorite hobby is writing poems, children's books and short stories. There have been many people and many books that have influenced her throughout her journey.

Rachel (Randi) Gerber

The Story: The Bird
THE BIRD

THE BIRD'S PERSPECTIVE

I am most fortunate! I have the honor of being the king's favorite bird. I sit near his throne, ever ready to do his will. He delights in my beauty and in my song. Sometimes he gives me small tasks to do. It is all I could ever want.

And yet, sometimes I wonder …

Many, many centuries ago, the king, who was beloved by his subjects, feared that the harvest would not be accomplished on time. To make sure that the harvesters would be strong and well, he gave them of his bounty before the harvest. This was not the usual procedure; usually the harvesters worked well together, and then celebrated after the harvest.

Nevertheless, they enjoyed his generosity. But in their extreme enjoyment, they lost track of the time. They missed the harvest deadline.

The king then was angry with his people - angry and disappointed with them.

But in his kindness, the king sent his people a tzaddik to tell them how to win back his favor. The tzaddik instructed them to capture the king's favorite bird, and to offer the bird as a gift to the king.

The subjects were happy to do this. But humans are fallible, and sometimes inept. They did not work together to capture the bird. And so, the bird escaped.

You may guess who that favorite bird is ... it is me!

The king told me to leave the palace, and fly down to the kingdom. The people glimpsed me, and were enthralled with my beauty and song. They all saw that I would make a beautiful present. They tried to capture me, to offer me as a gift to the king.

But I am not an earthly bird, I am a royal bird. The king set a spell on me, so that I would entice the people to capture me, but ... they may capture me only if they worked together, as they had done in prior harvest times.

Because they failed to do this, the king has still not forgiven them.

They are still his special, holy nation.

Over the years and years, the king sends me down to the kingdom, and the subjects get a glimmer of my sparkling wings as I soar by. They are allowed to hear my elusive trill. But, try as they may, they never capture me.

Over the years and years, many of the king's subjects have forgotten about him. They don't even notice my presence. Or if they do, they don't remark on it. They are busy serving themselves, or other leaders that they have substituted for the king in their hearts.

This is unutterably sad to me.

I wonder when they will finally capture me. Because they must. They must.

The king no longer requires that all of his subjects work together. That is no longer possible. But he waits for enough of them to work together. He yearns for closeness with his beloved nation. He watches them and waits still.

And I wait with him, praying that this day of rapprochement and reconciliation will come sooner than soon.

THE PEOPLE'S PERSPECTIVE

This tale is still told among some of our families.

One pre-harvest time, many, many centuries ago, we had a king. He was beloved by his subjects, and gave us generously of his bounty before the harvest. This was not the usual procedure: usually the harvesters worked well together, and then celebrated after the harvest.

Nevertheless, we enjoyed his generosity. But in our extreme enjoyment, we lost track of time. We missed the harvest deadline.

As a result of our missing the harvest, the king was angry with his people. Angry and disappointed with them.

But in his kindness, the king sent us a tzaddik to tell us how to win back his favor. The tzaddik instructed us to capture the king's favorite bird, and to offer the bird as a gift to the king.

The subjects were happy to do this. We glimpsed the bird, and were enthralled with its beauty and song. We all agreed that it would make a fine and beautiful present for our king.

But humans are fallible, and sometimes inept. We did not work together to capture the bird. And so, the bird escaped.

Because we failed to appease the king, he has still not forgiven us. But we are told that we are still his special, holy nation.

Over the years and years, some of the subjects have said they saw a glimmer of sparkling wings of a bird soaring by. Some say they have heard an elusive trill.

Over the years and years, many of the king's subjects have forgotten about him. They are busy serving themselves, or other leaders that they have substituted for the king in their hearts.

To those of us who still tell this tale, this is unutterably sad. We have not forgotten our beloved king.

We still yearn for closeness with him. We wait still.

We wait, praying that this day of rapprochement and reconciliation will come sooner than soon.

It is well-known that Hashem is everywhere.

But Hashem especially desires to have a home with Am Yisrael, here on earth.

When we were in the desert, starting our transition from being Bnei Yisrael to Am Yisrael, Hashem instructed Moshe Rabbeinu to build the Mishkan, a place where the two Tablets of the Law would stay. It would also be the resting place of the Shechinah, Hashem's presence among us, even as we journeyed to Eretz Yisrael.

Hashem directed Moshe to assign the job of architect specifically to Betzalel. What is particularly remarkable about this?

First, Hashem was clear in his choice of architect, so much so that He even referred to him by his name. Quite an honor!

Second, Betzalel was a 13-year-old bar mitzvah boy. Why would Hashem entrust such an awesome task to such a young man?

Betzalel was young, he was innocent, he was inexperienced. These were not failings; rather they were positives. He was uncorrupted, unblemished, and eager to take orders from Hashem.

And he came from exceptional lineage. His great-grandmother was Miriam, sister of Moshe Rabbeinu and Aharon HaKohen, whose confidence in and devotion to Hashem were unrivaled. His great-grandfather was Calev ben Yefuneh, one of the two spies who praised the land of Israel. His grandfather was Chur ben Calev, feisty and courageous, who died al kiddush Hashem at the hands of the rabble while protesting the creation of the golden calf.

Hashem chose this particular, innocent young man, knowing that he would accomplish the work with holy devotion and exactitude. His purity was a blessing. Hashem Himself would provide Betzalel with all the training he required.

Hashem could have chosen anyone to build the Mishkan. His choice of Betzalel ben Uri ben Chur for the job was simplicity itself.

About the Author

A jack-of-many-trades (computer analyst; web designer; and special ed./early childhood teacher), in early spring 2020, newly single at the age of 61, Rachel made the commitment to be a Torah Jew and never looked back. While waiting for Mashiach, she mostly spends her days in prayer, learning, tikkun, and shopping online for tzniusdik clothing

Debbie Druce

The Story: The Exchanged Children
TIVERIA

Rebbe Nachman's story, The Exchanged Children, begins with the birth of two baby boys on the same day. One is born to the king and queen; and one son is born to a maidservant and her husband who work for the king and queen. The midwife who delivers these infants, deceives the mothers by exchanging the maidservant's son and the king's son. The maidservant's son becomes the king's son and the king's son is raised by the maidservant. The parents, unwittingly cheated by the midwife, are troubled by their sons' adolescent development. As for the boys, they are oblivious to this deception when they are children, but as they mature, their souls become troubled and restless.

Each young man is vexed by the gossip about his true birth parents. Each son loses his ambition to actualize his life. The "king's son" (born to the maidservant) wanders away from his responsibilities as a ruler, and the "true king's son" (raised by the maidservant), becomes destitute and takes on a job as a cattleman in an effort to better himself. In a dream-like forest setting the desperate true king's

27

son enters the forest as he chases after his runaway cattle, and the lazy maidservant's son enters the forest chasing after his runaway horse. By coincidence, they meet each other and become buddies. A nightmarish experience ensues. They sleep high up in a tree and hear animals moan through the night, and strange sounds of laughter shake the trees at dawn. A moment of reprieve eventually comes to these young men.

At what point does Rebbe Nachman jolt us to a new level in order for us to be able to relate to these men's plights that deepens our consciousness of our lives as Jews? That moment of reprieve when the true king's son meets "the Man of the Forest" inspired me to write this essay, in response to the prompt, "On what merit can a person inspire a soul to learn Torah?" For now, I'll take you on a journey to Tiveria.

There is a place by the shores of Tiveria where the foundation of a shul built in the early 1800's stands. The shul, covered by heavy overgrown vines and surrounded by large slabs of gray, cracked pavement, demarks a promenade for street vendors to sell souvenirs to tourists like me. Thankfully, early this morning, going for a walk feels promising. I'm intrigued to see the contrast of the bizarre pieces of junk strewn around the shul's premises, to discover a view high above the town's marketplace.

When facing the shul's entryway, I look left and see a steep sloping hill jutting out, and perched on the plateau in broad daylight, are the graves of Rabbi Akiva and Ramchal. Then, above their graves, stands a large yeshiva from where I hear sounds of the yeshiva children noisily arriving and beginning their tefillot above the din of cars and delivery trucks passing nearby me.

I look from that high point down to the shul's locked entryway, and wonder if this spot below where I am standing was juxtaposed precisely by the builders, and by the congregants, so they could be inspired by that holy spot above, as well as the sparkling morning view of the Kinneret, as the sun rises above the eastern shore in the distance. This is a mysterious city, with footsteps of Tzaddikim, a place full of Tzaddikim and mystics. But who knows? There is no one to tell me this morning.

Understanding the layout of Tiveria is exasperating for outsiders like my husband and me, coming to visit. The city is surrounded by high rolling hills and vistas. As we descend into the city from those high rolling hills, we traverse the winding streets that seem to lead us nowhere. We can only persist through this maze of dead ends until we reach the bottom of the city, along the shore, where the old, excavated walls meet, and the new hotels crowd the view of the Kinneret.

I discover the best way to understand the layout of Tiveria while setting out to visit the peak where Rabbi Akiva and Ramchal are buried. Suddenly, as one looks down to the shoreline and out to the sea, then looks right to Rabbi Meir Baal HaNeiss's kever, left to Rambams's kever and then farther beyond to Mt. Hermon towering in the distance, the panoramic view is majestic, and the truth of the city unfolds.

Standing by Rabbi Akiva's grave I think to myself how Rabbi Akiva was unique and a true inspiration to being a Jew today. Rabbi Akiva was martyred by the Romans in 135 CE. We are taught that at his death he said, "I have always wanted to fulfill the true meaning of the Shema, and now with all my heart, with all my soul and with all my might, I can."

Rabbi Akiva absorbed the barbaric torture and suffering to come in this Common Era. His teachings are everlasting.

Rabbi Akiva's life began as an uneducated man who worked as a shepherd, but at the age of 40, he began to teach himself to read and to study the Torah. While a shepherd he met Rachel, the daughter of a wealthy Jewish landowner. They married despite Rachel's father's protests. Rabbi Akiva loved his wife Rachel and attributed his success as a great Torah sage and leader to her.

As children, we learned how Rachel endured the hardships of poverty and ridicule to sustain her husband in his mission. We learned many parables said by Rabbi Akiva, such as the one about the fox beckoning the fish to jump out of the water to escape the fisherman's snare and the story of the fox exiting from the rubble of the Beit Hamikdash.

The song we sing for Lag B'Omer, the enigma of Rabbi Akiva in B'nai Brak in the Pesach Haggadah: "What was Rabbi Akiva thinking the night of the seder when his students reminded him, "Rebbe, it is time to say the morning Shema!"?

Rabbi Akiva admonishes us and beseeches us to love our friends like ourselves for he knew the divisiveness of the Jewish people, the tragic consequences of sinat chinam. He lived shortly after the destruction of the Beit Hamikdash and learned among the great sages of his time. The Romans hunted down Jews for teaching Torah. Rabbi Akiva was persecuted for his teachings and his leadership to support Bar Kochba's rebellion.

No other religion can compare to the truth and fortitude conveyed by Rabbi Akiva. His teachings far outweigh the Christian teachings said to originate in the locale where I stand. Rabbi Akiva absorbed the pangs of the Messiah, the suffering shared by Jews living throughout the history of this Common Era. Here, the persecution and suffering to come; the self-sacrifice and kiddush Hashem of our fellow Jews in the Holocaust; the joys and love demonstrated in the Jewish home; the learning of Torah and the mitzvoth which connect us to our Creator; and the promise to return and to rebuild this land and to sanctify our lives rings true.

Here at these graves in a voice so quiet and yet so loud, I hear, "We exist today as Jews, wise because we believe in our Torah, and vulnerable because we are human. We stand here in Israel and as a people returning to and fulfilling God's promise. Our mission is galut."

I walk next to Ramchal's adjacent grave.

31

In contrast to Rabbi Akiva who began his Torah study at age 40, and lived over 2,000 years ago, Ramchal was born in Italy in 1707, and died at age 40 in the Holy Land, two years after settling there with his wife and children. Ramchal, at the age 19, mastered the Kabbalah and developed a following, yet he was often persecuted and rejected by established Rabbinic circles. Ramchal wrote, Mesilat Yesharim, a book to instruct us on how to refine our character traits. His piety, intelligence and deep understanding for his fellow Jews continues to influence people today. He followed the footsteps of early "Lovers of Zion" the kabbalists of the 1600's, and the mystics of the Vilna Gaon, who came in the 1730's and who began building stone shuls along the Kinneret. Almost like father and son, Rabbi Akiva and Ramchal stand together; a beacon on a hill, shedding light to wandering Jews in the Diaspora and here in Israel, helping to sanctify their daily lives with integrity, dignity, compassion and joy.

Rabbi Nachman must have traveled to Tiveria to be with his fellow mystics and pray at his forefathers' graves. What did he want to convey to us?

Rabbi Nachman, born in 1772 in the Ukraine, was the great grandson of the Baal Shem Tov. Rabbi Nachman's mother Faiga was a pious woman who inspired her son at an early age to understand the ways of tzaddikim. He suffered much to learn the way of tzaddikim and to transmit this knowledge to his devoted disciple Rabbi Nosson, who recorded his teachings and stories for posterity.

Rabbi Nachman's trip to the Holy Land lasted many months, until his return to his wife and children in the Ukraine. He traveled through the deep forests of Europe, to the shores of Istanbul and finally to the shores of the Holy Land. Rabbi Nachman captures that moment of respite for the wandering true king's son in The Exchanged Children, after a dream-like sleep. There in the forest, he meets the Man of the Forest. Stunned to see the sprightly man in this mystical forest, the younger man asks, "Who are you?"

The man replies, "Stop chasing after your sins!"

He continues, "I live in a place that no one comes to, a place of my father's, father's forefathers..." and then pointing to the sky, he says, "I live there, a place reached by passing over snakes and scorpions."

How can I not associate these statements with coming to Israel? I add to this line, "a place of dreams, a place of prayer, a place for actualization and fulfillment. The desperate king's true son and his sleepy companion rise up and reach the forest-man's abode. They sit and eat and sleep there. They feel refreshed and ready for new challenges: to express dignity and integrity.

Ramchal and Rabbi Nachman, who lived over two hundred years ago, understood the plight of modern man, feeling disconnected from his surroundings and searching for his lost soul. Nafshi cholaat, my soul pines. Rebbe Nachman admonishes us and pleads with us to trust the guidance of tzaddikim like himself to bring us brachot of fulfillment and understanding to our lives. He brings to light the personal and historic travels in exile and the yearning of the heart to return to a close relationship with our Creator, to be united as a people and rebuild Zion.

"On what merit can a soul steer the body to bring Torah to the world?"

In Tiveria, this is a place to contemplate such wonders and such truths, and in Rabbi Nachman's stories ... "V'Ahavta et Hashem Elokecha."

I wrote this piece Erev Lag B'Omer in 2021. This final draft does not have the joyful consistency I conveyed in the beginning. However, I felt happy I could connect to the holiday by thinking of Rabbi Akiva. Actually, from that day, our world has changed and is reeling with tragedies and changes that appear to be accidental. And many of these "accidents", including those related to my personal stage in life (visiting my elderly parents, coming to terms with my mother becoming handicapped and losing her strength, and so on). Hashem is good to us. There is so much more I wish to say in order to crystallize these moments in time and bring alive the true goodness of why we endure now and in the past.

HITBODEDUT AND A TRUE DREAM

I love being outdoors. Every morning I try to walk and be alone to discover Hashem's majesty in the clouds, the sky, in the light beaming on the trees and to hear the birds sing as I peer more closely to discover nature's wonders and to connect with Hashem and to understand myself.

Many times, I am afraid of losing myself in nature and I will forget what needs to be done and then I question if I am really communing with Hashem or if I should pray in the formal way with a siddur. Rabbi Nachman recommends Hitbodedut. Although Hitbodedut comes naturally to me, there are many times that I cannot escape to the outside to muse, sing or exercise.

Dreams help me understand deep experiences or relationships. I have not had those kinds of dreams lately. But my husband did today.

He dreamt that he was back in England living in a house in Cheetham Hill, and he saw a plane descending which looked as though it was going to crash. It disappeared behind the trees, but there was no sound as it hit the ground. Suddenly Howard saw his father open the door to (our) house and quietly stand there. Howard said to me," Dad looked thinner, but it was him! He had on his hat and dark raincoat, he was silent and looked concerned. But then he looked at me and our eyes met, and we reached out and we hugged each other."

When Howard told me this dream this morning, I said, "Of course, today is Rosh Chodesh Iyar and the eleven-month aveilus, mourning period will be completed later this month. "As soon as Howard described how Dad looked, I immediately felt his presence; and a connection that I have not felt since he died, a palpable connection I longed to feel this year.

What does the plane descending mean? Or its descent to Cheetham Hill? Or us meeting in Cheetham Hill? Did the plane crash mean Dad's death and his expression showed the pain he felt?

Dad (my father-in-law) came to visit Howard by plane, a way to connect heaven with earth. Cheetham Hill represents Dad's place of origin, the once flourishing Jewish community in Manchester where Howard's parents and their siblings grew and worked, and where Howard fondly recalls his childhood days. And now, thinking of last year, and the year before, when we visited Dad? We accompanied him walking to the tiny Cheetham Hill minyan three flights up in a small room with a rickety old floor on the third floor of the Jewish Federation building; a minyan of men hanging up their raincoats, and hats, and jostling, fondly remembering those days using siddurim with names of people who filled their lives and the streets of Cheetham Hill.

The plane? I often think that when a person passes away, if one sees them, a deep conflict is released. For us, coming to the US and leaving my in laws in England was a big conflict.

When my father-in-law died, we could not visit him. Howard could not help him in the hospital or attend the funeral. The essence of my father-in-law was his independent nature, and he loved to walk by himself.

My father-in-law came back to say goodbye to his son and to re-assure him and thank him for saying Kaddish so carefully and so consistently.

To forgive? No, but to tell Howard and reassure him that his father wanted to live on his own, and be as independent as possible, but he missed his son very much and hopes Howard will be well and remember their bond.

I asked Howard if I was part of this dream. "Yes, we were living in the house in England."

This was perhaps the wish or the regret we never fulfilled or really could have fulfilled. That time in life or the place which none of us could return to.

And that hug?

In that dream we were there in England, but I think that Dad came here and showed his love for us.

The Story: The Seven Beggars

GROWING UP AND SINGING ADON OLAM

"I am extremely old, but I am completely young. I have not yet begun to live, but nevertheless I am very old." The Exchanged Children, Rebbe Nachman of Breslov

When we were children, I asked my father, "How come we are called, Bnei Yisrael, the Children of Israel? When you grow up aren't you big and old?"

My father looked at me and smiled. My grandfather looked and said, "That is a wise question. You will see as you grow up, God still thinks of us as children, as His children." Dad added, "Bnei Yisrael are the children of Jacob, the sons who left Egypt in the Exodus, but now we are called, "Jews, Yehudim." Many of us asked the same question to our Hebrew school teacher. He corrected us by saying, Bnei Yisrael is what we were called long ago in the Torah. Now we have our own state, Israel, pronounced, ISS-rael, the modern way."

Some of my earliest memories as a child begin with staying up in bed at night and wondering who I am and where I would be in time. I would lie in bed and try to understand how the universe is infinite with no beginning or end. I would stay up thinking of the years I would grow, each step like a ladder according to the grades of school, and the people who were older than myself, like Faye our babysitter, four years older than me. I would wonder again how the universe can be infinite and how do we come to be here, and do we have to die? To me the world began with me, and any history before me was long ago. I would get up in the morning and sing that I was a princess, and someone would find me, and the birds outside were singing good morning, too.

We read fairy tales of faraway places, illustrated *Andersen's Fairy Tales*, *Grimm's Fairy Tales*, and *Aesop's Fables*. There were several books about Jewish children: one, *Little New Angel,*about the birth of a new baby brother and *The Shabbat Queen,* which described the beauty of the Shabbat table and welcoming the Shabbat Queen to our home. These were lovely stories we read with our grandparents on Friday nights. Other times, I would sit in my father's study, and he would give me illustrated books about Ruth or Jonah and the Whale as well as illustrated Hebrew books with strange figures I couldn't understand.

But *Hansel and Gretel* was one story that dominated my childhood imagination. The story became an operetta which we listened to often. You probably know the story of the two children who were forced into the woods by their harsh stepmother, where they encounter a witch who enslaves Gretel and locks Hansel in a cage to fatten him up for her cooking pot. After some time, Gretel bravely pushes the wicked woman into the oven where she dies, and Hansel, along with other children, is freed. Their woodcutter father finds them and brings them home. Everyone is happy and dances, and sings, "With my feet I click, click." So did we, in school, with the music teacher. Later, as an adult, I read a story by Agnon about a peasant woman living in the German forests, who did macabre things to lone travelers in the forest. But as children, we were oblivious to the undertones of this tale or the calamity of Jewish life in the Holocaust.

The first chapter of *The Seven Beggars* begins with Rebbe Nachman saying, "I will tell you how people once rejoiced," and then describes how the king crowned his son king during his own lifetime. He tells his son to be happy even when he faces troubles. The king's son devotes his attention to acquiring secular knowledge and he loses his simplicity. He becomes an atheist like his advisors and they all "forget the art of war." However, when a war breaks out and the townspeople flee, a boy and a girl from separate families are abandoned in the forest as their parents runaway. The lost children are hungry and sad. A beggar meets them, and they follow him in the hope he will help them. He is kind to them and gives them bread. They realize the beggar is blind. The beggar says, "I do not want you to go with me, but I will bless you that you should grow to be like me, and old like me." Another beggar comes and another, until a total of seven beggars help the children survive. Each beggar has a defect and each one blesses the children and says they should be like him. The story takes us along throughout the children's lives, and tells us how they make their livelihood as beggars. How, as they grow up, a colony of beggars, encourage them to marry. The story takes us to a child's dream come true of meeting one's true love and getting married to live happily ever after. But there is so much more. When the wedding takes place, the young couple desires that the same seven beggars return to bless them at their wedding. Miraculously, each of the seven beggars appear on time and bless them. Will the beggars' blessings shield these children from life's troubles? Can these married "children" bring the blessings we pray for; blessings of peace and unity to the world? Does this story symbolically reveal ideas about our Jewish history, our heritage, our ancestors? What makes us change from being children to adults?

I remember going to Hebrew School and synagogue with so much excitement. I wanted to learn more about the stories I had learned, such as Miriam saving her baby brother Moses or Esther becoming Queen. Our shul was located up one tall flight of stairs, with an entry from a building along a side street we could walk to from home or school. Sometimes kids coming to shul would bring their bicycles up the stairs and take them down after services or Hebrew school with a bumpitty bump. On Shabbat, we would walk down the wide flight of stairs with others and the Schpers would walk next to us.

Looking back in time now, I wonder, "What did the Schpers feel inside as all of us charged up and down with so much youthful vitality, often still singing Adon Olam and not knowing about suffering and loss? The Schpers cherished us and wanted us to live life fully. The Schpers loved us. They kibbitzed with us and were generous with their time to talk to us and to invite us to their home. Their daughter Faye would babysit for us. But we kids wondered, "Why did Nat have a white pupil in one eye?" "Why did Rachelle speak in a heavy accent?" Little by little, we learned about their past. Their life stories seemed to make them old.

Nat became blind in that one eye with the white opaque spot in place of a pupil because a German Nazi hit his eye with the rifle butt, when he was fighting with the partisans in Poland. Later in life, at age 48, he became totally blind. But one would not know he was blind. He went to classes. He stood next to Rachelle, his wife and conducted conversations as though he could see. Because he could see – he could see through to the heart of a person. He loved listening to voices and to people's accents. He loved Yiddish. He came from the city of Warsaw, a melting pot of Jews speaking Yiddish from all different places. He said to me in the kindest way, "I remember your grandmothers' accents. Your father's mother spoke with a Litvak accent. Your Grandma Sarah spoke with an old-time, rare Romanian accent. In that instant, I felt Grandma Sarah's presence as though she was alive, wearing that wide banded ring with small diamonds and a ruby in the center. I heard her voice clearly reprimand us with, "Put your shichlech on your feet or you will catch a cold" or with enthusiasm, "Sit down for lunch and have some pickles," but they were really cucumbers. Or "Have some huckleberries," but they were blueberries; and when she was tongue-tied, "I forgot," and scolding my brothers with, "Behave! Do not be a bulvan!" Much later, when Grandma was very old, she looked outside the window and talked to me about the people she loved, saying, "Life is like a song. You can feel it, but you cannot hold on to it forever."

When the beggars bless the married couple, each one recounts an aspect of creation and conception which I describe in these loving relationships, as well as many others in my childhood. These nurturing relationships helped us develop spontaneity, curiosity, and trust. But as children, we were also wild, and we misbehaved. We learned to lie and cheat and be disrespectful. How does that kernel of truth and wisdom and wonder we sense as children sustain us as we grow older? Tragically, that trust and innocence can be so severely broken and destroyed. The fragile seed can be nurtured and flourish, but suffering, abuse and bad influences can destroy it.

There is one more story I want to add. I want to include my neighbor and friend who passed away this year. She loved Hassidic tales. There was so much I never understood about her but now I do. I found her books of Rabbi Nachman's tales which I use for this class. I found among her mother's personal belongings a folded piece of paper from the nursery school teacher describing her daughter's interaction at school with her teachers and classmates. This note opened a window to my friend's childhood. The little girl that I wanted to know, perhaps that little girl inside me wanting to be friends like Faye was to me. Perhaps because her mother knew me when I was raising three sons, and at my wits' end about how to deal with everyone including myself. With insight and humor, her mother wrote me a prescription, "Deborah Druce needs one hour a day to do whatever she wants, especially gardening, which she loves." I tacked that prescription to the refrigerator and referred to it every day. If I find it again among my saved papers, I will put it in a frame and hang it on the wall.

And this is what I hope to do. I hope to keep that kernel about her family, which my friend loved and missed so much. I discovered this kernel so that now it seems to be part of my childhood and my upbringing, and I can accept all the difficulties of family and the mystery of living in this world.

About the Author

Deborah Druce lives in West Orange, New Jersey with her husband Howard. Deborah and Howard met each other in Haifa, Israel in 1973, when they attended a World Zionist Organization Conference for College Students Worldwide. They married in 1978 and first lived in Manchester, England, Howard's home, before moving to New York, Maryland, Missouri and finally to New Jersey where they have lived in West Orange for 29 years. They have three sons, two who are married, and three grandchildren. Deborah has worked as program coordinator for seniors in her community as well as coordinating women's learning, and teaching children and teens in special ed. She loves to garden and observe nature, study Torah and be outdoors walking.

Your Turn

We invite you to try your hand at a Breslov warm-up prompt on the topic of simplicity designed to get your writer's inspiration flowing.

Rebbe Nachman often develops themes by introducing us to unique connections between two or more bechinas (ideas or concepts.) Simplicity is an important theme in his teachings, as are humility and emunah, which are motifs in the Rebbe's famous story, The Sophisticate and The Simpleton. A Breslov leader of the previous generation, Rav Levi Yitzchak Bender, says that the entire path of the Rebbe is hidden in this story in which two close friends take very different paths in life. The Sophisticate, with his intelligence and philosopher's mind, seeks out prestigious career choices and luxury. He puts a lot of energy into refining his tastes until only the finest things will satisfy him, which naturally leads to suffering since the finest things are not always available. He is disappointed again and again, when the world doesn't live up to his standards.

The Simpleton becomes a shoemaker and is satisfied and happy living a humble life. He cobbles together mediocre, odd three-cornered shoes, which people won't pay much for. The namesake of this journal, the three-cornered shoe can be understood to be a heartfelt expression of the unique spiritual self. The Simpleton is satisfied with his handcrafted shoes, simple meals, old sheepskin coat, and frequently expresses to his wife his delight with and gratitude with for his life. He also believes in something bigger than himself, which enriches his life with deeper meaning.

Although a casual reading might suggest that the story is about the conflict between the desire for material success vs. the contentment that comes with living a simpler life, the story contains many layers. We must remember that Rebbe Nachman had many pious followers in his audience; followers who were mostly likely not terribly interested in social climbing or life's fleeting material pleasures in the first place. Though they likely understood some of the deeper, mystical meanings of the story, what might they have gained from the simpler telling?

In addition to lack of faith, the desire for honor and corresponding lack of humility, are perhaps the most significant downfalls of the Sophisticate. Was the Rebbe hinting to the idea that even pious individuals might prioritize the intellectualization of Torah study or extravagant expressions of piety, in order to gain honor? This seems to be alluded to in the more tongue-in-cheek, Yiddish colloquial usages of the terms for the main characters: Chacham (a wise, knowledgeable person vs. a know-it-all) and Tam (innocent, sincere person vs. a simple, ignorant person.) Although it's easy to be attracted to the sheer brilliance of Rebbe Nachman's teachings, the Rebbe encourages us to serve Hashem with simplicity because, after all, "God is ultimately very simple," no great intellectual feats or over-the-top stringencies required.

The story also is about being happy with our spiritual level, even as we aim to grow. The shoemaker is satisfied with, and even happy about, the imperfect shoes he crafts, although his work does not bring him much money or any honor. When we learn that the shoes themselves can be seen as a symbol of one's spiritual service of Hashem, especially prayer, as well as one's own imperfections in general, we are introduced to the very Breslov theme of being joyful despite one's flaws, the idea of truly feeling happy with our lot -- Ashreinu! Much of the shoemaker's joy is rooted in this simple happiness; in not desiring or pursuing honor for himself, leading the reader to ask herself what importance honor has in her life. After all, we live in a world today where the search for honor and its partners – success, fame and power – are so much more easily facilitated than they were 200 years ago. There's no need to travel to gain recognition – just pull out a phone or laptop and voilà – external validation is literally in the palm of one's hand. But the Rebbe encourages us to believe in ourselves, along with belief in Hashem, His Torah, and the true Tzaddikim. Each of us has a Sophisticate and a Simpleton inside, and with careful reading of this one story alone, the reader has enough personal growth lessons to last a lifetime.

Suggested reading: The Sophisticate and The Simpleton from *Sippurey Maasiot* by Rebbe Nachman of Breslov.

Warm-up Prompt: Write a letter to a close friend, or your past or future self, inspired by one of the Breslov teachings on simplicity, below. Will your letter inspire or offer advice? Will you confide and share what you have been thinking about, feeling, and experiencing regarding simplicity in your own life? Will you bring your own Torah knowledge into your letter? Will your letter touch on simplicity as it relates to the world at large and the times in which we live?

Choose to include one or more of the following as inspiration for your letter on simplicity:

When [the Simpleton] finished making a shoe, it would all too often turn out triangular as he was not fully proficient in his craft. But he would take the shoe in his hand and praise it greatly. He would take enormous delight in it, saying, "My wife, how beautiful and wonderful this shoe is. How sweet this shoe is. This shoe is pure honey and sugar!" *The Sophisticate and The Simpleton, Sippurey Maasiot*

The essence of Judaism is to conduct oneself in pure innocence and simplicity, with no sophistication whatever. *Likutey Moharan II, 12*

No sophistication is needed in serving Hashem - only simplicity, sincerity and faith. Simplicity is higher than all else. For Hashem is certainly higher than everything else, and Hashem is ultimately simple! *Sichot Haran (Rabbi Nachman's Wisdom)*

Throw aside all wisdom and clever ideas and serve Hashem with simplicity. Make sure that your deeds are greater than your wisdom, because the main thing isn't learning but its practical application... When it comes to serving Hashem, even a person whose head is filled with genuine wisdom should set it all aside and serve Hashem simply and innocently. *Likutey Moharan II, 5*

Debbie Rubinstein

THE SEVENTH BEGGAR

Rabbi Nachman doesn't tell us what happens when the seventh beggar comes to the wedding and tells his story. I've imagined it happening like this:

The children yearned for the seventh beggar, who was the beggar without feet, to come to their wedding.

Suddenly, he made an appearance at the chuppah. He had come to give the young couple his blessing. Everyone noticed he wasn't touching the ground; it seemed he was floating in the air, soaring as if he had wings instead of feet. The beggar approached the young couple and began to explain.

"I have feet but only use them to perform a mitzvah." And, he continued, "I am walking with them but you can't see them because you are my main objective; when you are in need of a blessing or a helping hand, you can't see clearly, you are confused and bewildered."

48

"My feet are here," the beggar added. "They're so light and airy, they become weightless and without any limits. I can use them to glide on the road and get to my mission in the beat of a pulse."

The beggar with no feet began to tell the wedding party a story: "There was once a child in danger. He was all alone in the dark woods, without any food or hope of survival. I then heard about him and traveled in a rush to help that lonely child find another lost soul, another child also wandering in the wood. They were now together and they cherished each other. They needed help. I sent six angels in the shape of beggars that provided them with food and hope.

"These angels are here today. They have already given you blessings and now it is my turn. I'm meeting you on the most important day of your lives, the day you become one. Today I want to give you a wedding gift, the bracha that you should be like me, with light feet, to fly and run to fulfill a mitzvah, to aid a soul in need, and on your way to do so, you will not touch the mud on the ground. You shall only be carried by the holy melody you will hear in the air."

Everyone at the wedding rejoiced, and the bride and groom delighted in all of the blessings they had received.

The Story: The Treasure
THE TREASURE UNDER THE BRIDGE

Tall and strong, connecting two ends, hovering over constant moving current that never dies, the bridge allows me to rest my hands on it and not fall into the waters.

I try to catch with my eye swimming shadows and my own reflection stares back at me. I then look up and see the other blue, with its warmth and a few cotton clouds.

Right in the middle I can see the beginning and the end; I choose to return to the starting point with all those life expectations. This time knowing I'll find myself again in the middle of my journey, but now I will decide how I will traverse the bridge.

Will I always have the enthusiasm to go on?

What perspective will I have within reach? Can I modify the cadence of my steps on my way to a better middle? Would I want to start over?

Yes, of course! The end is still not here, I will evoke for myself an even better crossing, one with no finishing strokes, just beginnings.

The story of Trust is a story about Power and Resilience.

The power to become the unstoppable fixer, there are no closed doors for him.

The one who finds strength in knowing the Divine Intervention.

The one who sees the dancing flame behind the bonfire.

The one who connects with the energy that moves worlds.

The hurdles we face are the shadows behind the fire; we are so vulnerable. Yet, the obstacles lead us to our next step.

Never too comfortable, we need to constantly renew our found happiness. These are the footprints we need to follow.

The decayed roof and the dancing notes of a violin; the sword that becomes the magnanimous forgiving component, due to the sharpness of a mind!

Happiness is so personal, so is depression.

I choose not to go to the dark corners,

I want to stay in the center of fixing,

In the responsibility of freedom.

We can try to find the solution to almost every stubborn unopened door; let's not lose sight of that airy opened window waiting to be explored.

We don't know how strong we are until we take risks. God has given us the sword and the fallen roofs; we are able to persist with our beliefs.

About the Author

Debbie Rubinstein was born and raised in Mexico City and now lives in Newton, Massachusetts. She is married with a family and has a degree in Art History. In her free time, she writes, does photography and makes food art.

Naomi Mass

Background note: My experience in the Breslov Writing Class has been like none other. Chaya Rivka's invitation to contemplate and formulate personal reflections in class, and on paper, was a creative and spiritual venture that I could not resist. Since my first class, I felt I'd found a new sense of joy in my purpose.

Over the course of several months of attending class, however, the process of writing proved painfully awkward. When it came time to write, it felt to me that others were "on their marks, set and ready to go," while I was still contemplating our conversation and the depths that Rebbe Nachman's story traveled. (Later I learned that everyone had their own pace.) Eventually, I found that the experience of being guided through the layers of the stories of Rebbe Nachman felt like putting pieces of my soul in their correct place, along with the odd sense that I hadn't known I needed it!

In this piece I tried a poem format. It felt like the cadence enabled my personal reflections on the story to surface more easily.

The Story: The Exchanged Children
DRAWER FULL OF SUNSHINE

Like the beautiful songs that emanate
From placing the instrument on the beasts of the forest,

And the way the moon waits quivering in the darkness
'Til it receives its garments from the sun,

My soul awaits a fixing,
Its burden to be subdued.

But, oh, how my physicality refuses
To be sublimated by my Soul Drive,
Could it be as easy as selling that part of me
For a piece of sustaining bread?

The Forest Man tells me
The answer isn't found along the road I'd taken,
All doom, gloom, and criticism.

I take his advice to make a drawer for life's
Preoccupations, worries and pain,

I've gone and made another one
Filled with somersaults, laughter and joy.

I'll open my little drawer of sunshine,
To find the Godliness that's within me,

Then it will step forward and conduct
The orchestra that is my life.

I'll rectify the Exchanged Souls,
By crowding out darkness with delight.

Background note: The things discussed in class are like gems and I try to capture them by taking notes, sometimes in a rapid poem format. This helps me keep track of my, and my fellow writers', comments and reflections on the teachings of Rebbe Nachman during the writing class. The notes, in poem format, help me to create references for what I will compose, once the conversation stops and we begin to write.

The Story: Simplicity
NOTES IN THE FORM OF A POEM AND THE HUNTING PARTY

Notes In the Form Of A Poem

The Baal Shem Tov said that in the future, the times we live in now, the simplest Jew who says *Tehillim* with sincerity will be as rare as the greatest Tzaddik.

Rebbe Nachman stopped in Istanbul on his way to Eretz Yisrael.
He rolled up his pants and ran around acting like a foolish child,
Playing war with the children in the street,
Foolishness with a higher intent, rearranging Napoleon's war perhaps.

Even the King has been affected by the state of the world,

Drenched in a river of atheism.
We forget who we are, so many stories of being lost
Who will remind us of who we are? The simple peasant will.

The Hunting Party

I am one of the King's trusted ministers.

I am honored to have served him for many years. I was chosen from his elite army at the tender age of 18. Since that time, I've been a trusted aide, invited to join him on his hunting parties.

We hunt for wild animals as a prize, and as a show of our mastery over nature. It's always a jubilant time, and a tremendous joy to assist the King on these expeditions.

We return victorious on our steeds, laden with wild game found in the palace's forests; deer, partridges and sometimes wild boars.

Our most recent hunt was unusual in several ways. It quickly became one of the worst days of my life. But as you will see, it ended with me learning something from the King that could not have been learned otherwise.

I woke in the barracks, before sunrise, to prepare for the hunting party - boots polished, horse fed and groomed, both of us in our finery. When the King emerged in the courtyard, he was unrecognizable at first. Instead of his royal attire he was clad in leather pants and an oil cloth jacket, "The better to focus on the hunt!" he said. There are also dangers on the way home (as we once saw in the unfortunate attack by a highwayman on the Duke of Upstart). With the King dressed as a simple rider, he would evade the notice of bandits or rebels.

Once the other ministers joined us at the royal stable, we spread out in formation. The fine foxhounds ran ahead. I remained close behind the King, as my saddle carried His Majesty's personal belongings. Spirits were high and there was much bantering between the ministers, each of us anticipating our prize.

As we approached the forest at the far end of the King's property, each of us diverged from the center and spanned out as far as the eye could see. Suddenly, the sky blackened and rain fell so hard and fast that I could barely see or hear my fellow ministers. Each ran willy-nilly for cover, so as not to ruin their finery. I did not know where to go and then the horror set upon me: I had lost sight of the King!

The rain would not abate and very quickly the forest flooded. I mumbled a prayer that I should find the King, but I was distracted by my drenched clothing and concerns about my horse who was not accustomed to these conditions. Foresight, my horse, struggled to get us through the quickly rising river of mud, until I was able to steer us towards civilization to find shelter."

I reasoned with myself all the while: My King is a wise and experienced woodsman; surely he will find shelter and not be swept away. It grew darker still; night was also approaching, but finally I came upon a warm dry inn at the edge of the forest. I left my horse to feed and recover in the stable, but I could not rest nor eat all that night as the rain continued to fall. I was tormented by my lapse of duty, miserable over losing sight of the King. Needless to say, my fine wool, boots and medals had been ruined by the rain.

That night in bed was fretful. Where was the King now and how could I have left his Royal Majesty out of my sight? I cried. What would he think of my faithfulness now that I failed? I know I lost esteem in his eyes, and my own. How can I remedy this?

When daylight arrived. I found the other ministers, dry and sleeping in front of the fireplace in the front of the inn. Not one had seen the King. And I, like a wet mutt, had not taken care to dry my clothes. How could I without knowing the wellbeing of my beloved King and close friend?

After a hasty breakfast, we spread out to scout the forest. Eventually one of my fellow ministers gave out a loud hoot. In a small clearing, in the middle of the forest, was a tiny cottage with a thin stream of smoke coming from the chimney and there, standing in the doorway, stood the King. He withheld his anger as we approached. "How could you abandon me in the flood, each running to cover themselves?" he bellowed. "Do you not know your place and whom you serve?" Several of the ministers tried to explain themselves and urged him to return with them to his castle. "I will not hear of it!" he thundered. "No matter your objections. My host, this kind, simple woodsman who took me in, fed me a bowl of warm kasha, and gave me his straw bed, will have the honor of accompanying me back to my castle in his wagon."

And that is what happened. This was how I learned that even when there is a great tumult and confusion, we must always remain faithful to the King and seek him out. And that the simplest form of reverence and honor, a bowl of kasha and a straw mattress offered with a full heart, are worth more to the King than elegant, vain formalities. Oh, what a hard way to learn! For we had scattered and forgotten him when there was danger, while this simple man remained faithful through it all.

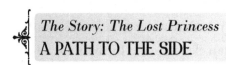

The Story: The Lost Princess
A PATH TO THE SIDE

Feeling very far from wholeness reminds me that I'm closer than I was,
Everything seemed simpler when questions went unanswered
Now the more I strive to serve Hashem by day,
The longer my bedtime list grows.

There were no goals or bucket lists
When I set out from the family home to explore,
To immerse in another culture,
The one behind me felt corrupted.

After each elegant storied land had been visited,
Croissants and pastry tasted,
A path to the side eventually appeared
Barely known, yet ancient, it had always been there.

Decades later, bleary-eyed, I wash last night's coffee mug,
A blessed break from spike proteins and confusion,
Our trusted ministers, once relied upon, have fallen into chaos
With a single gesture, I press pause, and choose to replay today's mini
Torah lesson.

In time, belongings get broken, grown out of, used up and moldy,
But the essence of my creaky futon still persists, holding guests who
sleep over.
Dented and tarnished candlesticks still hold holy light,
Swollen knees and fingers are nimble enough for marathon Shabbos
preparations.

60

*Torah Vav, its letter comfortingly straight and tall,
Represents the symbiotic dance between my chosen actions
and Heaven,
Of the unearned gifts showered straight down upon me,
And the date of my birth into this world.

There's a Nikuda Tova, a good point, also in the moment,
I encourage myself to find the silver linings
So very many needs to get through, though just as much uncertainty
Holding tight to Truth and Mitzvos as trusty vehicles for the path
I've chosen.

On this narrow bridge are found layers and layers of yearning,
Much like the Viceroy's, to overcome temptation, to carry out the
King's will,
Even the wanting to want is good enough,
On the path of my soul's completion.

*Lesson Six in *Likutey Moharan*, which is traditionally learned as a
preparation for Rosh Hashanah but can be learned any time.

In the Water Castle my true essence will be sheltered
A comfort when I'm brought to the edge
I can always escape to it, like the Lost Princess, run and
Rather drown, than be caught and imprisoned.

To the Other Side my purity is a prize,
Whether I die fleeing is no matter to Him
If I slip as I flee, I may live the rest of my days as His captive,
If I forget the Art of Waging War, it's on me.

"His arrows shooting day and night,
They come from far and long ago
Will I succeed?
I'm surrounded in every direction, but I must get inside.

With my own moyach I can choose,
For this chase is never ending,
To run to the Water Castle and wash myself clean,
May the Beggar Without Hands always pull my arrows out.

About the Author

*Not so long ago, there was a freckle-faced girl with blue eyes who
dreamed of visiting faraway places. When she got older, her dream
came true and she was introduced to her soulmate in the City of Lights,
at the intersection of two roads going uphill, and they quickly ascended*

to Yerushalayim where they were married. After some wandering, they settled in a home on the edge of a forest in a shtetl called Monsey where she was blessed with raising their children and grandchildren. She divides her time now between her Functional Genomic Nutrition practice, studies and homemaking.

Sarah Shoshanna
(Charlene) Hakimi

Dear Beggar with the Crooked Neck:

Our wedding day was something much more than a dream. It was a time and place of holy freedom. The holiness radiated from every person, including my groom and me and the rest of the beggars, especially the seven special beggars. Each one of you granted us a gift, and I want to thank you personally for yours.

Being a beggar has not been easy. Sometimes, I feel happy that I am chosen to be a beggar and sometimes, when my da'at leaves me, when I look at life the way the rest of the world does, I get sad. When I see how poor I am and how rich others are. When I see the competition and the battles.

But your gift has changed me, and it's changed my husband, and our marriage. Because sometimes, when I don't have the words to express what I want to say, when all I have is a sound, a note, a groan, or a grunt, I remember there can be beauty in my wordless cry. I know how to use these sounds. I know not to write them off as unimportant but to use them. It feels like I learned how to play the piano that is this world and how to get close to Hashem with my feet still on the ground.

Thank you, dear beggar with the crooked neck, for opening the door to the possibility of true righteousness. May it be that everyone knows of this path and uses it to unlock their treasuries of closeness to The Holy One.

Yours truly,
The Bride

The Story: The Lost Princess
WHERE IN THE WORLD AM I?

I look around and am so confused. I sense that something is deeper than what the world suggests but I don't know what it is. Why would I need to look deeper? It seems like the answers are on the surface (sometimes.) But I do look deeper. I look over and see the path to the side. My path to the side is the path to my truest and highest self, to the pleasure that I have always been waiting for, to true closeness to Hashem, to true life: the path to the Bat Hamelech.

What I have come to learn about the path to the side is that it is a private path, a secret path, and a precious path. This world stresses fame, success, honor, and respect, but these goals have nothing to do with any path to Hashem, all the more so my path to the side. The Evil One puts in overtime to make sure that finding Hashem on the path to the side seems like an unimportant task.

Once you finally start on the path to the side, Hashem takes you on many journeys, and it's easy to forget that you're looking for the Bat Hamelech. Who is She anyway? But you continue to search... search. Then, there are times when you are actually close to freeing her, and you must gather all of your strength to stay alert, keep yourself awake, breathe, know who you are, what your mission is, and who your Boss truly is.

But it could be those times are the times that all you want to do is to stop. (Can't I just lie down in the corner? I'm tired of this journey! Give me a moment or two to rest.)

I think I've finally found the Bat Hamelech! Let me talk to her. I've been so lonely. "How did you get here? How can I get you out?"

But when you find true gold, do you stop and cherish it in the middle of a busy street? Or do you only stop to cherish it when you have hidden it in a safe place? In that one moment when no one is looking, grab her! LEAVE! YOU'RE ALMOST THERE! Don't be afraid to win. You can win.

And if you haven't won yet, it's okay. Remember: Where in the world am I? I am in the palace of the Lo Tov. I am searching for the Bat Hamelech. I will free her and take her home.

Amen.

The Story: The Lost Princess

THE DEFINITION AND IMPORTANCE OF YEARNING

Yearning is a feeling that I didn't have the words for, a longing that left me feeling out of place, not in control. I was ashamed of it. I thought it had no place in this world. Why would I feel this way? "Surely something is wrong with me," I thought. I felt out of place in this world that values DO DO DO. Because what could I do with this thing called yearning? What could it bring me in this reality?

The undercurrent of Rebbe Nachman's story is yearning. Yearning is what drove and led the viceroy to success. Yearning is not easily understood, too simple to grasp. Yearning is the silent parts of the soul that only Hashem sees. Yearning is what drives a person, but yearning can be lost self-esteem, without a belief in me, an invisible charge that is tearing my heart open and forcing me to look inside where the truth lies.

I yearn for the Golden Mountain and the Pearl Castle. They do exist. I can choose to save the Lost Princess and reunite her with The King of All Kings.

About the Author

Sarah Shoshanna (Charlene) Hakimi works as a Pre-Toddler teacher. She enjoys dancing and writing. She attends Seminary on the weekends and also invests her time in learning and living the Rebbe's teachings.

Leah Osnat (Linda) Zulberg

If I lived
In a little house
Suspended in the air,
I wouldn't have a care
For there
is no sadness, no stress, no emotional mess
No misunderstandings in the illusions and delusions of the
challenges of life.
Every single thing I needed
All the guidance sorely needed
It all sounds Divine
and I feel so full.

Far from the choices that bombard my mind and my heart –
exhausting me,
and leaving me somewhat uncertain if that choice indeed should
have been made,

in that place, at that time.

Would it have been better after all, to have given in and done it?
Or not given in and not done it?
Not felt it?
Not even thought it?
In my little house, it could be an easier life,
Relieved of the suffocating strangulation of uncertainty and strife.

No need for revision upon revision in the clarity of sound above
the ground.
Nothing Earthly in this Ethereal place,
this Supernal space
devoid of the compulsion of the infernal chase...

Here, there is no need to "understand one thing from another"
To try to fathom
what happened in Meron and why?
For all is one
and all is GOOD.
Because up here we know,
and we think as we should -
And the tragedies of Centuries
and the tragedy of Meron...
Joy and Devastation and the need to answer why?
They all don't exist
in the house in the sky.

But I need to leave this elysian bliss and get back to my physical task –
my task in the garden,
the garden that requires my trying to understand one thing from
another.
For now 'tis the time for gardens and gardening:
for planning and planting and ploughing the land,
for pruning and trimming to make it look grand.
So much goes into the work in the garden.
And so it is, six days each week:
For six days I garden with focused intent,
Propelled with inspiration of the day I have spent
up in the air with Kedusha and prayer -
with clarity of Ratzon Hashem up there.
The Brocha is
that every week, every week without fail,
the Shabbos Queen arrives as a Gift for me…..
And together up, up and up we flee
For our day of Menucha, where the air is so fair
held in the Holiness of my little House in the air.

The Story: The Prince of Gems
YOU CANNOT HAVE IT ALL

Was it not enough
all the Blessings that she had?
Beauty, talent, wisdom –
shouldn't these have made her glad?
Elegance and eloquence,
a maestra with winds and strings,
The centre of attraction for foreign dignitaries and Kings.

The envy you're feeling Princess, is not unique, not strange,
It's the acting out that's the problem, because there's nothing you
can change.
You, oh beautiful Princess endowed with innate Gems,
Look, Your Highness, look at yourself and see through a grateful lens.

How low
do we really need to go
to avoid the ripples of Kinah?
Those ripples
can tipple
and cripple our dreams,
prodding us, like you, to disastrous schemes.
For soon, it's not only the Kinah that's there,
it's the Ka'as and Kavod and Taivah that snare:
all fitting partners to contaminate our air.

I'm no oracle,
nor do I pretend to be.
But, young lady, surely you can see
the truth that's known Universally:
Envy destroys
ENVY DESTROYS:
It chips and it chips and it chips till it breaks
dragging you down to drown in sour grapes.
Leave your brother, he is the Prince,
be content with your own dazzling brilliance,
He is the longed for, rightful heir to the throne.
Let him be who he is or you'll end up alone.
Let him sparkle,
Let him shine,
What Hashem wants for him
Can ne'er be thine!

The Story: The Exchanged Children
HALF A PACKAGE OF BREAD

He sold himself for bread?
For a shared packet of bread?
Was the dread so strong?
Would the bread bring so much pleasure
That he voluntarily said he would sell himself forever?
How can this be?
It's impossible to see
the reason for this totally irrational plea.
Yet Esav did it
and Haman as well,
For a temporary relief, they bid so much of themselves farewell,
only to regret it later,
to howl with remorse;
with profound regret
when they realized just what had been lost.
Perhaps it was an innate awareness of their inappropriate status
and a deep subconscious need to rectify the malpractice?
And what about us?
See how we make a fuss –
Blinded
by our own impulsivity,
as we drown in compulsivity
and our own subjectivity -
thinking about
what we deserve because
she has got a nerve
to want what is mine.

And again, we sell ourselves to prove we are right,

caught in the clutches of Ta'avah, Ga'avah, Kinah and Sina's overwhelming might.

Yes it is me, me, me: it is all about me –

Oh why can't we see this curious oddity?

So we yearn

to learn

to integrate the lessons -

to do T'shuva, through contrite, deep confessions.

We grow to value ourselves and what Hashem has given.

And do my best with what I have

and treasure my gifts from Heaven.

Oblivious to his blindness,
they gratefully eat the bread -
Basking in his kindness,
unaware that he's impaired.

Yet he seems unhampered, by his unseeing eyes -
doing his duties in the dark, with determined ease.
He aims to assuage the children's cries
with compassion, he leaves them appeased.

He cannot see
and yet, he can –
Indeed, perhaps better than the average man.

He doesn't seem to struggle
in the muddle
of the darkness,
of the black,
Yet he doesn't feel the loss of light
Of what we think he lacks.

For we are blinded because of our sight:
Our vision isn't clear:
It's many a year since the clarity of the lamp's light
in the womb:
and its glow has all but disappeared.

So we are left grappling with our ta'avahs and our middos
With our blurred perception and unawareness of how we can
overcome this.

So, we need to ask the question:
Are we alive?
or are we dead?
It seems that we all need that special bread
to give us a meaningful life:
To satiate and save us from our inner and outer strife

About the Author

*Leah Osnat (Linda) Zulberg lives in Johannesburg, South Africa. She
is involved in various activities of the Jewish Community including
learning and giving Torah Classes and Kiruv programs. She writes
and directs Theatrical Musical Productions for women and girls. Each
play has valuable Jewish lessons for the performers and the audience
as they work together with the help of Hashem. She thoroughly enjoys
participating in Chaya Rivka's writing workshops. Leah Osnat is so
grateful to Hashem for the opportunities He has given to her.*

Shulamit Michal (Susan) Strassburger

The blind beggar says, "I am extremely old, but I am completely young. I have not yet begun to live but nevertheless I am very old." I think what the beggar says defines how life works much of the time. There are periods where we move through life like the king's son, jumping on the wings of fresh excitement, seeking wisdom, and gleefully grabbing academic knowledge and new ideas. Our eyes take it all in. We feel wise. We feel mature. Sometimes, we feel old beyond our years. And then Hashem speaks to us. His messages are always personal. We all have them and it's true that closing our eyes enables us to hear those messages better. Blocking out the world, there's Hashem's tug to the heart. There's that nagging question, "What am I doing here? Is this really all there is?" It's Hashem's presence that slows us up allowing us to recognize our Neshama's lack. We find ourselves starting again with Hashem, younger.

The Story: The Exchanged Children
TO MY DEAR CHILD

Dear Child,

You asked me how I came to be where I am now. That's a very good question. Sometimes, I don't know.

What I do know is that when I was a young adult, I didn't feel that I had a place in the world. It seemed unfair because I pretty much listened to my parents, graduated from college, and worked at a job I liked; things I always knew I was supposed to do. And if I had done these things that I was supposed to do, why didn't I feel better?

I felt I was always up against people I didn't fit in with. I was just meandering, bumping into trees I didn't see in the dimness, the thick branches, heavy with leaves, blocking the sky.

One night, my mother was going to a Sisterhood meeting at the shul where my brother was taking Bar Mitzvah lessons. This was out of character, because my mother didn't go to shul, was not religious and still isn't. When she asked me if I wanted to go along with her, I said, "Yes," because I had nothing else to do.

The shul's new, young Rabbi didn't have a beard which surprised me, and his face was one of the kindest I ever saw, and even though he was a bit heavy, he bounced around the shul full of joy. He was just so glad to be with us.

We sat in the sanctuary listening to the Rabbi speak from his pulpit. It's been too many years for me to remember exactly what he said, but I remember being drawn into his words about God's relationship with the Jewish people.

After his speech, the Rabbi came over to speak with me, which I found amazing (I guessed at the time it was simply because I was a new face). After I told him I had never been to his shul and didn't know anything about Judaism, he still talked to me and, he listened to me. He suggested a book for me to read, and offered to discuss it with me.

We met in his office where, in his soft-spoken manner, the Rabbi explained basic tenets of Judaism, answered my questions, and opened my mind. My ideas about religion started changing. I no longer saw it as rigid and irrelevant but instead, elastic and current. I felt like Alice stepping through the Looking Glass into a flipped world.

My journey to where I am now started on that night. It hasn't always been easy or enjoyable. Sometimes I find myself at odds with people who have no interest in religion or my journey. Sometimes I wish that the Looking Glass would flip me back out so I no longer would have to deal with this, but, and rightfully so, I don't think it's built to do that.

I believe God orchestrated that shul event and my presence there, and I believe that the Rabbi was God's agent. God is always leading us, bridge by bridge through life. And please understand. dear child, that God doesn't build a bridge just to blow it up while we're crossing. He builds it to carry us forward.

With love, from me to you,
Grammy

The Story: The Sophisticate and the Simpleton
CAN'T BEAT TIME

I have had arguments with time since childhood; the school year went too slow, summer vacation went too fast, not enough time to study for the test, the test time flew... Nothing changed in adulthood - couldn't something be done about that nine-month long pregnancy? Time moves us along to our various plateaus in life. Arguing with time can lead to the belief that you have some control over it.

At each plateau, the Sophisticate fights time in his unwillingness to accept where he is (standing). Where he is never good enough. He always looks to his next step, to the future. Assuming he has time and control of it is central to his character. He admits this when the subject of marriage comes up. "But this is not my concern now. I will have plenty of time for this in the future."

When the Sophisticate receives the letter from the King summoning him, he begins his conflict with time.

The first thing he says is, "Wait," stopping his progress, trying to stop time. The King summons him - he resists, questioning the King's existence. He grabs time by its throat forcing it to his will. Time retaliates, in the guise of the Devil, by throwing the Sophisticate into a quicksand bog, immobilizing him. There is nothing the Sophisticate can do on his own to get himself out. He is stuck where he is for the first time. There isn't an argument that will make a difference; nothing he can control.

He must live in the present, as we all must.

The Story: The Exchanged Children
OUR MOST IMPORTANT SEARCH

(At the end of the story everything is arranged in its proper order.)

We need to strive for everything arranged in its proper order. I believe arranging things in their proper order is among the reasons God brought us into this world. This world challenges us because all the pieces and their meaning, lovingly given to us by God, are scattered. Throughout our lives we search for these pieces, shuffling along on what we think is our forward path, but it's hard to know if we are right. How do we know when we have lost our way? How do we know when things have been turned upside down?

It's easy for me to believe the slave's son becomes the king while the king's son becomes a slave. Living in "Opposite Land" can seem normal. We pick up the pieces we find, put them together as best we can, and believe we have placed them correctly. When we're confronted with a dilemma, we gather the pieces we have at hand. From these pieces, we figure out what we know, and use that knowledge to make our best decision what to do. I do not believe that the average person wakes up any day and decides to purposely make bad decisions.

This is how we make our way along, sometimes with clear paths, sometimes bumping into obstacles that knock us far from where we are. It's tiresome and occasionally can be dangerous. If we could just find that person, that event, that will give us the key enabling us to understand where all our pieces truly belong, we will never get lost. Searching for the Forest Man and the Man Riding a Horse can be long and hard, but it's the most important search of our lives.

The Story: The Lost Princess
DON'T GIVE UP

Rebbe Nachman tells us the secret to accomplishing something – "If you want, you do." I have a magnet on my refrigerator – "If you really wanted to, you would."

We never find out why the King's precious daughter falls into such disfavor with him, that he said the Evil one should take her away. But she did, and she was taken away. The viceroy stood up and went to search for this precious daughter. For me, he's searching for Hashem, searching for Torah, searching for mitzvot, searching for anything that would bring him closer to Hashem.

His journey is fraught with failure, in the beginning much from his own missteps. He has exact instructions what to do to rescue the princess, much like we have Torah and mitzvot to guide us in life. But he veers off track, doing what he should not: He falls asleep when he needs to stay awake, he drinks wine when he was specifically told not to. Seemingly small things trip him up, just like small things trip us up. The viceroy doesn't give up, just like we should not.

Eventually he finds the giant of the winds who can help him, though he doesn't help him immediately. The giant calls all the winds to see if any of them knows where the princess is. There was one wind that was late, but it was only late because it was taking the King's precious daughter to the Golden Mountain and Pearl Castle. This wind, although late according to the giant of the winds, was right on time according to Hashem.

The viceroy never gave up and Hashem orchestrated everything for his success. Was this because he never gave up? I think so.

About the Author

Shulamit Michal Strassburger is a retired mother and grandmother who worked in IT for close to 35 years. Now, she's challenging her right brain with writing and painting. She is also studying Torah and the Hebrew language. She has been published in magazines and literary anthologies and was the second-place prizewinner of the Breslov Research Institute writing contest in 2018, for which she received a complete Breslov library.

Glossary

Abba; Heb. father

Adon Olam; Heb. lit. Master of the Universe, refers to a hymn which is part of the daily prayers

Aharon HaKohen; Heb. Aaron the High Priest

Am Yisrael; Heb. The nation of Israel (the Jewish people)

Ashreinu; Heb. Happy are we! A very popular Breslov niggun is from this verse of the morning services: Ashreinu ma tov chelkeinu umah naim goralainu Happy are we! How goodly is our portion, and how pleasant is our lot…

Aveilus; Heb. Mourning in general, the 12-month period of mourning

Avot, pl; Heb. lit. fathers, referring to the Biblical Patriarchs

Azamra; Heb. lit. I will sing/make music, refers to Rebbe Nachman's famous lesson in Likutey Moharan, 282, as well as the concept of

Azamra described in the lesson – to look for the good point in others and one's self; the Tzaddik "composes" a beautiful melody of these good points

Baal Shem Tov; Heb. lit. Master of the Good Name; 18th century founder of the Chassidic movement and great grandfather of Rebbe Nachman of Breslov

Bar Mitzvah; Heb. when a boy becomes obligated in the Torah commandments at age 13 (Bat Mitzvah for a girl is at age 12)

Bat Hamelech; Heb. Daughter of the King, princess

Beit Hamikdash; Heb. The Holy Temple of Jerusalem

Betzalel, Betzalel ben Uri ben Chur; Heb. Chief artisan of the Tabernacle

Bitachon; Heb. Trust (usually trust in God)

B'nai Brak; Heb. Ancient city in the Hebrew Bible

Bnei Yisrael; Heb. Children of Israel (the Jewish people)

Bracha/Brocha/Brachot, pl; Heb. Blessing, blessings

Breslov; Heb/Yid. A small town in Ukraine (Bratslav) which Rebbe Nachman designated as the name by which his teachings, movement and followers would be known

Bulvan; Yid. Boor, uncouth person

Calev ben Yefuneh; Heb. Caleb from the Torah

Chidush/Chidushim, pl; Heb. new/original ideas, usually referring to new ideas in Torah thought

Chizuk; Heb. encouragement

Chumash; Heb. Five Books of Moses, Pentateuch

Chuppah; Heb. Wedding canopy, wedding

Emes (Emet); Heb. Truth

Emuna; Heb. Faith

Emuna Peshuta; Heb. Simple faith

Eretz Yisrael; Heb. The Land of Israel

Erev; Heb. Evening

Esav; Heb. Esau

Esther; Heb. (Queen) Esther

Da'at; Heb. Knowledge, Holy awareness of the Divine

Faiga (Fayga, Feiga); Yid. Lit. Bird, Rebbe Nachman's mother's name

Ga'avah; Heb. Arrogance

Galut; Heb. Exile

Geula; Heb. Redemption from Exile, the Jewish people's spiritual-national return to Eretz Yisrael

Guf; Heb. Body

Hakadosh Baruch Hu; Heb. The Holy One, Blessed be He

Haman; the villain of the Purim story

Hashem; Heb., lit., "The Name", a way to refer to God by the Holy Name without using the name indiscriminately

Hasidic/Chassidic; Heb. The name of a movement and those who follow Chassidic teachings which emphasize prayer, joy, faith, love of God and love of others, etc., founded by the Baal Shem Tov in the 18th century

Hishtadlut; Heb. Usually refers to material action one must take in addition to spiritual action, though Chasidim consider prayer (including Hitbodedut), giving of charity and repentance to be hishtadlut as well

Hitbodedut; Heb. lit. seclusion/isolation, talking to Hashem in your own words, in private, as you would a best friend about whatever is on your mind and in your heart, especially but not limited to spiritual matters; prayerful meditation; Rebbe Nachman emphasized the importance of hitbodedut and taught that it was central to achieving spiritual growth

Imahot, pl; Heb. Mothers, referring to the Biblical Matriarchs

Ka'as; Heb. Anger

Kabbalah; Kabbalistic; Heb. The Kabbalah is the name for the wisdom of the mystic, inner Torah, recorded in numerous texts across the centuries

Kaddish; Heb. Here, referring to a specific prayer of mourning said for one's close relative

Kavod; Heb. Honor and glory

Kedusha; Heb. Holiness

Kever; Heb. Gravesite

Kiddush Hashem; Heb. A sanctification of Hashem's name through a moral action that inspires others

Kinah; Heb. Jealousy

Kinneret; Heb. The Sea of Galilee

Kohelet; Heb. Ecclesiastes, a book of the Hebrew Bible written by King Solomon

Lag B'Omer; Heb. lit. The 33rd day of the Counting of the Omer, a day when the mourning of the Omer period is lifted

Likutey Halachot; Heb. The Collected Laws, a Jewish masterpiece by Reb Noson, Rebbe Nachman's leading student, scribe and follower. It offers explications of the deeper meanings of Jewish law illuminated by Breslov teachings, Jewish mystic and psycho-spiritual thought

Likutey Moharan; Heb. (the Collected Teachings of Our Teacher, Rabbi Nachman), Rebbe Nachman's magnum opus, part one (286 lessons) and part two (125 lessons), containing multi-layered teachings on Jewish mysticism, personal growth, ethics, Jewish practice and law, prayer, and more

LM; Abbreviation for Likutey Moharan

Lo Tov; Heb. Not good

Mashiach; Heb. Messiah

Mefarshim; Heb. Commentaries

Menucha; Heb. Tranquility

Meron; Heb. Mountain near the holy city of Tsfat where a grand Lag B'Omer celebration is held, and the site of a tragedy in recent years

Mesilat Yesharim; Heb. lit. Path of the Righteous, an ethical work by Rabbi Moshe Chaim Luzzato

Middos; Heb. (also middot) Here referring to personal attributes and character traits that are considered positive

Minyan; Heb. A quorum of 10 men needed for public prayer

Miriam; Heb. Moses' sister

Mishkan; Heb. The Tabernacle, the portable sanctuary the Jews carried in the desert

Mitzvah/Mitzvos/Mitzvot, pl; Heb. Commandment, There are 613 mitzvot

Moshe Rabbeinu; Heb. Moses our Teacher

Moyach; Heb. Brains, intellect

Nikuda Tova; Heb. Lit. the good point, referring to the point of Divine connection inside and the eternal soul which yearns to please Hashem

Neshama; Heb. Soul in general and specifically the third level of the soul and/or a Jewish soul

Noach; Heb. Noah

Pasuk; Heb. Verse

Pesach Haggadah; Heb. The text recited at the Passover seder

Rabbi Akiva; Heb. A Tanna, a leading and beloved teacher of the Mishna in the 1st and 2nd century CE, and a Jewish martyr

Rabbi Meir Baal HaNeiss; Heb. lit. Rabbi Meir Master of the Miracle, A Tanna, a leading and beloved teacher of the Mishna, today people donate to any one of *numerous charities in his name which give their proceeds to the poor of Israel*

Rachel; Heb. Rachel of the Bible

Rambam; Heb. Acronym for Maimonides, Rabbi Moses ben Maimon, a 12th century scholar, Jewish philosopher and physician

Ramban; Heb. Acronym for Nachmanides, Rabbi Moses ben Nachman, a 12th century scholar, kabbalist, and Biblical commentator.

Ramchal; Heb. Acronym for Rabbi Moshe Chaim Luzzato (see Mesilat Yesharim)

Ratzon Hashem; Heb. lit. The Will of God

Reb Noson (Reb Nasan, Rebbi Natan); Reb Noson Sternhartz, born in 1780 in Nemirov, Ukraine, was a great Jewish scholar and spiritual seeker. Yearning to become closer to Hashem, he sought answers from the Chassidic mystics and eventually found Rebbe Nachman. He became the Rebbe's student during the last eight years of the Rebbe's life. Reb Noson was Rebbe Nachman's main scribe and most important follower, and according to the Rebbe himself, the primary reason why the Rebbe's works were published and distributed. Reb Noson devoted his life until his death in 1844 to spreading Breslov Chassidut, despite tremendous hardship. He was also the prolific author of numerous original works of halacha, prayers, Kabbalah, and letters, which were based on, or referenced, the Rebbe's teachings, and are scholarly and inspirational master-pieces in their own right.

Rebbe Nachman; Rebbe Nachman was born in 1772 in Mezhibuzh, Ukraine in the home of his great grandfather, the Baal Shem Tov, founder of the Chasidic movement. The fresh approach of Chasidut re-vived ancient Jewish concepts that had gone into hibernation through-out much of the diaspora, concepts such as: joy's essential role in per-sonal spiritual service; the Holy One's love and compassion for even the simplest person; the importance developing a relationship with Hashem; and many other life-changing teachings. From his earliest childhood Rebbe Nachman, a unique thinker extraordinaire, em-braced these concepts and began to bring forth numerous new ones, forming a body of work unmatched in intellectual and spiritual depth and breadth. The teachings of Rebbe Nachman and his early followers are as fresh and relevant today as they were two centuries ago. His lessons are passionately conveyed through brilliant intellectual explo-rations of virtually every topic in Judaism, deep mystical revelations, and unique pairings of themes and ideas; fascinating stories that veil great Kabbalistic ideas which are the inspiration for the writings in this journal; and powerful practical advice. Rebbe Nachman passed from this world in 1810, but two centuries later, more and more peo-ple continue to attach themselves to him through visiting his resting place in Uman, Ukraine and studying, meditating on and applying his wisdom. Those that do, find solace in their struggles and relief from heartache, doubts and confusion. Most of all, his teachings strengthen our faith and help us live lives of joy – they heal the soul.

Rosh Chodesh Iyar; Heb. The New Month of Iyar (Rosh Chodesh is a monthly semi-holiday at the start of each new Hebrew/Jewish month)

Rosh Hashanah; Heb. lit. The Head of the Year, Jewish New Year festival, a profound holiday of intensive prayer, self-reflection, as well as joy and celebration

Sefer; Heb. book

Sefirot; Heb. In Jewish mysticism, the sefirot are an interconnected group of 10 Divine vessels, attributes or powers through which God is manifest in creation.

Shabbaton; Heb. A gathering for the purposes of inspiration and Jewish togetherness during an entire Shabbat

Shabbat; Heb. The Sabbath, a time in which we refrain from various creative acts, and spend time in prayer, singing, and togetherness with family and friends

Shechina; Heb. the hidden, feminine-aspect of Hashem also called the Divine Presence. She is in exile with us and will dwell once again in the times of Moshiach; today, the Shechina remains at the Kotel (the Western Wall of the Holy Temple,) still standing in Jerusalem

Shichlech; Yid. Shoes

Shul; Yid. Synagogue

Sichot Haran; Heb. A collection of discussions and teachings of Rebbe Nachman of Breslov

Siddur/Siddurim, pl; Heb. Prayer book

Simcha; Heb. Joy, joyous celebration such as a wedding or bar mitzvah

Sina; Heb. Hatred

Sippurey Maasiot (Sipurei Maasiyot); Rebbe Nachman's stories, the thirteen main tales, each of which contains very powerful soul-medicine

Shtetl; Yid. Jewish village usually in Eastern Europe

Taivah/Ta'avah; Heb. desire

Tefillin; Heb. Phylacteries

Tefillot; Heb. Prayers

Tehillim; Heb., Psalms, King David wrote and compiled these lyrical poem-songs; a book of the Hebrew Bible

Tikkun; Heb. Rectification, healing, repair, often spiritual

Tiveria; Heb. Israel's holy city of Tiberias on the Kinneret

Torah; Heb. May refer to the Five Books of Moses and/or the scroll it is written on by a scribe; the Hebrew Bible (Tanakh); the combined texts of Jewish wisdom, especially the Tanakh, the Talmud, and often the *Shulchan Aruch* (codes of Jewish law) and the Kabbalah; may also include works of Chassidut and Mussar (ethical teachings) and more;

an individual lesson/the body of work of a sage/Tzaddik, especially Rebbe Nachman's *Likutey Moharan*

T'shuva; Heb. (Commonly teshuvah), Repentance, to return to one's true self and authentic relationship with God

Tzaddik/Tzaddikim, pl; Heb. A highly righteous individual devoted to serving Hashem and helping individuals come closer to Him, the tzaddik has a unique role in Judaism in general, and in Breslov Chassidut in particular

Tzaddik Emet; Heb. True tzaddik, usually refers to Rebbe Nachman and sometimes other authentic tzaddikim of great stature; only a true tzaddik knows what a person needs to complete their teshuvah

V'Ahavta et Hashem Elokecha; Heb. "And you shall love Hashem your God," part of the Shema, the foundational prayer of Jewish faith said at various times of the day

Vayikra; Heb. Leviticus, Book of the Hebrew Bible

Vilna Gaon; Heb. Rabbi Eliyahu of Vilna, a great genius and prolific scholar of the 18th century, who was a leading opposer of the Chassidic movement, yet who, some say, eventually recognized that the Chassidim were bringing new life and light to the Jewish people of the times.

Yehudim; Heb. Jews, Jewish people

Yerushalayim; Heb. Jerusalem

Yeshiva; Heb. A Jewish school of religious studies for boys (generally junior-high through college age, sometimes also referring to the religious studies counterpart for girls)

Yetziat Mitzrayim; Heb. The exodus from Egypt

Yom Kippur; Heb. Day of Atonement, a Jewish holy day of fasting, teshuvah and great joy

Acknowledgments

It is with deep gratitude that I thank those wonderful friends whose material support made the production of this journal possible: Esther Ella Gurevich, Dr. Eleonora Goudis, Hilda Spektor, Naomi Mass, Debbie Druce, Shulamit Michal Strassburger, Sarah Shoshanna Hakimi, Evelyn Luchs, Debbie Rubinstein, and Rachel Gerber. May the merit of sharing Rebbe Nachman's incredible ideas and inspiration be a source of brachot in all your lives.

A truly fond thank you to Rachel Cohen, Sanam Movtady, Sarah Swartz, Evelyn Luchs, Rachel (Randi) Gerber, Debbie Druce, Debbie Rubinstein, Naomi Mass, Sarah Shoshanna (Charlene) Hakimi, Leah Osnat (Linda) Zulberg and Shulamit Michal (Susan) Strassburger the talented women who have generously given permission for their writing and artwork to be published in this collection. It isn't easy to put your inner world on paper and it takes courage and generosity to share yourself with others. Also special thanks to Rachel Cohen for permission to use her evocative painting, "Held" for the cover – I feel it captures the inner experience of reading and connecting with Rebbe Nachman's stories. Thanks also to Debbie Druce for her charming illustration, "Tiveria." May the merit of sharing your creative insights based on Rebbe Nachman's stories be a source of fresh insight in all of your lives.

Without those who have assisted with the production of this journal, it would have been a poorer publication indeed. Thank you to Rosally Saltsman for her professional and prompt proofreading. Many thanks to Naomi Mass for her help in the early stages of this project; Rachel (Randi) Gerber for her deft work editing the poetry of Evelyn Luchs and Sanam Movtady; and Shulamit Michal (Susan) Strassburger, for her relevant insights and editing, her exceptional organizational skills (including my personal Jabberwock, the dreaded spreadsheet), and her general willingness to jump in and do what needed to be done, with good humor and intelligence. May your participation in this experiential model of sharing Rebbe Nachman's life-changing teachings bring many *brachot* into your lives.

For the many teachers, publishers, commentators and translators whose works I've depended on to enrich my understanding, and subsequent teaching of the stories from *Sippurey Maasiot* as well as additional tales, commentaries and other texts, thank you to all including but not limited to: Rav Nissan Dovid Kivak, Rabbi Erez Moshe Doron, Rabbi Shalom Arush, Rabbi Avraham Greenbaum, Rabbi Dovid Sears, and of course, the classic translation with commentary of *Rebbe Nachman's Stories* by Rabbi Aryeh Kaplan, published by Rabbi Chaim Kramer and the Breslov Research Institute (BRI.)

While compiling this journal, Hashem gave me the test and gift of a severe health challenge which repeatedly interrupted the editing, production and publication of this project. I'd like to thank the writers for their patience. Also, so many people helped me during this time that it's impossible to name them all, but I would like to thank each of those kind friends and students who've been davening and saying *Tehillim* for me and generally keeping in touch with me – may Hashem bless you with everything good. Many thanks to Rav Elazar Mordechai Kenig, Rabbi Aharon Carmi and Mina Rut Haim of Breslev Tsfat for their prayers and encouragement. Sincere thanks to the Breslov Research Institute's Rabbi Chaim Kramer for his prayers and wisdom – his kindness and generosity and his commitment to spreading Breslov teachings have changed the lives of many people including me. A heartfelt thanks to my good friend and constant source of inspiration, Gita Kramer, who daily gives me chizuk and has enabled me, with her warmth and Breslov wisdom, to *never give up.* Thanks to my husband Moshe Chaim, who has supported me through the chaos of a few iterations of this journal and who has unfailingly been there for me. My gratitude to the Tzaddik Emet, Rebbe Nachman ben Fayga, whose stories and teachings have enchanted me, revived me and sustained me through life's ups and downs, knows no bounds.

Thank you to Hashem for everything and may we all merit to welcome the Moshiach very soon and usher in an era of health, joy and righteousness.

Chaya Rivka Zwolinski

Rosh Chodesh Shevat 5783 – January 2023